ED SHEERAN

WISE PUBLICATIONS
PART OF THE MUSIC SALES GROUP
LONDON / NEW YORK / PARIS / SYDNEY / COPENHAGEN / BERLIN / MADRID / HONG KONG / TOKYO

ED SHEERAN

PUBLISHED BY
WISE PUBLICATIONS
14-15 BERNERS STREET, LONDON, W1T 3LJ, UK.

EXCLUSIVE DISTRIBUTORS:
MUSIC SALES LIMITED
DISTRIBUTION CENTRE, NEWMARKET ROAD, BURY ST EDMUNDS,
SUFFOLK, IP33 3YB, UK.
MUSIC SALES PTY LIMITED
UNITS 3-4, 17 WILLFOX STREET, CONDELL PARK
NSW 2200, AUSTRALIA.

ORDER NO. AM1009800
ISBN 978-1-78305-784-9
THIS BOOK © COPYRIGHT 2014 BY WISE PUBLICATIONS,
A DIVISION OF MUSIC SALES LIMITED.

ARRANGED BY FIONA BOLTON.
EDITED BY JENNI NOREY.
PRINTED IN THE EU.

YOUR GUARANTEE OF QUALITY
AS PUBLISHERS, WE STRIVE TO PRODUCE EVERY BOOK TO THE HIGHEST
COMMERCIAL STANDARDS. THE MUSIC HAS BEEN FRESHLY ENGRAVED AND
THE BOOK HAS BEEN CAREFULLY DESIGNED TO MINIMISE AWKWARD PAGE
TURNS AND TO MAKE PLAYING FROM IT A REAL PLEASURE.
PARTICULAR CARE HAS BEEN GIVEN TO SPECIFYING ACID-FREE, NEUTRAL-
SIZED PAPER MADE FROM PULPS WHICH HAVE NOT BEEN ELEMENTAL
CHLORINE BLEACHED. THIS PULP IS FROM FARMED SUSTAINABLE FORESTS
AND WAS PRODUCED WITH SPECIAL REGARD FOR THE ENVIRONMENT.
THROUGHOUT, THE PRINTING AND BINDING HAVE BEEN PLANNED TO
ENSURE A STURDY, ATTRACTIVE PUBLICATION WHICH SHOULD GIVE YEARS
OF ENJOYMENT. IF YOUR COPY FAILS TO MEET OUR HIGH STANDARDS,
PLEASE INFORM US AND WE WILL GLADLY REPLACE IT.

WWW.MUSICSALES.COM

The A Team

Words & Music by Ed Sheeran

After meeting a girl called Angel when he played a Christmas gig for the homeless charity Crisis, singer-songwriter Ed Sheeran was inspired to write this song, based on her story. Released as the lead single from his first album +, it entered the charts at No. 3, becoming the highest-selling debut UK single in the first half of 2011.

Hints & Tips: While this is a fairly slow song, the melody is quite tricky in places. Play through the right hand a few times before putting it together with the left.

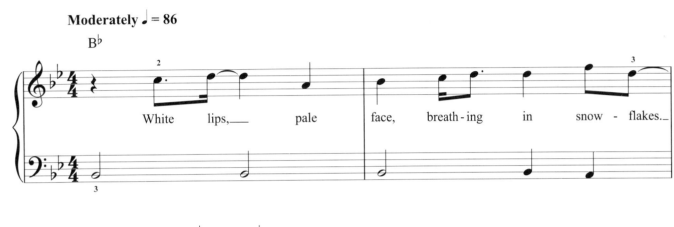

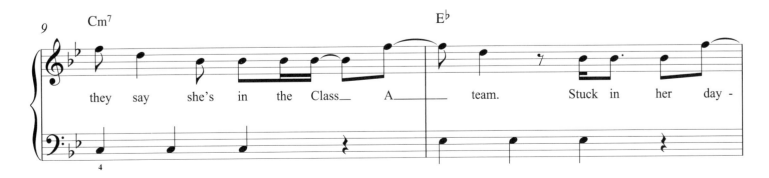

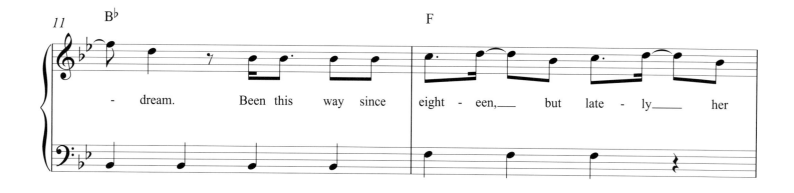

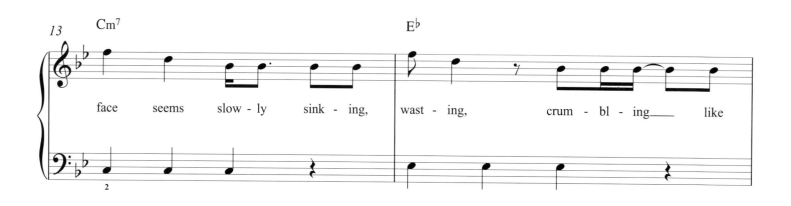

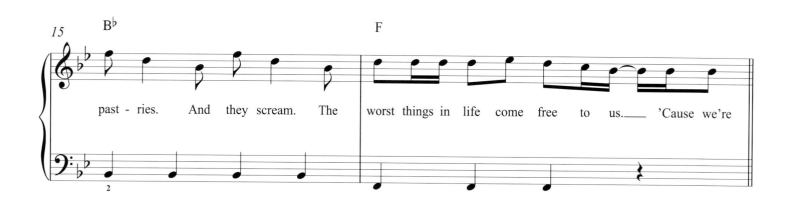

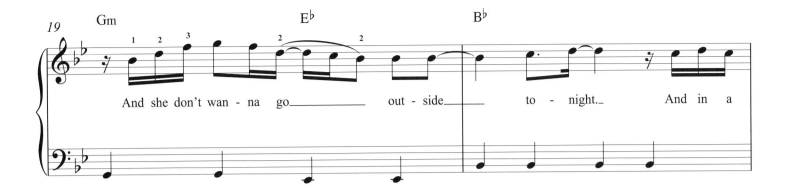

And she don't wan - na go_____ out - side_____ to - night.__ And in a

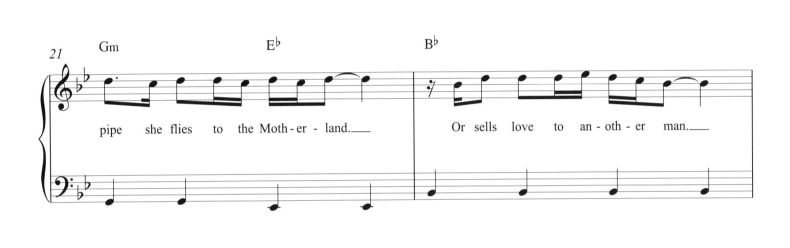

pipe she flies to the Moth - er - land.___ Or sells love to an - oth - er man.___

It's too cold_____ out - side_____ for an - gels to fly.___

For an - gels to fly._____

Afire Love

**Words & Music by Ed Sheeran, Johnny McDaid,
Foy Vance & Christophe Beck**

'Afire Love' is the closing track to the standard edition of Ed Sheeran's second studio album *x* and was co-written and produced by Johnny McDaid of Snow Patrol. The song is about Ed's late grandfather who suffered from Alzheimer's disease and sadly died just a few weeks after work began on writing the track.

Hints & Tips: Watch out for the tricky conflicting right and left hand rhythms in bar 11, practising each part separately until you're confident.

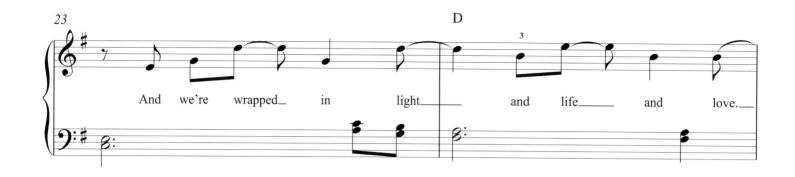

And we're wrapped_ in light_ and life_ and love._

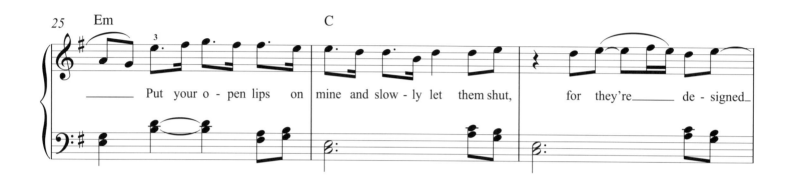

___ Put your o - pen lips on mine and slow - ly let them shut, for they're_ de - signed_

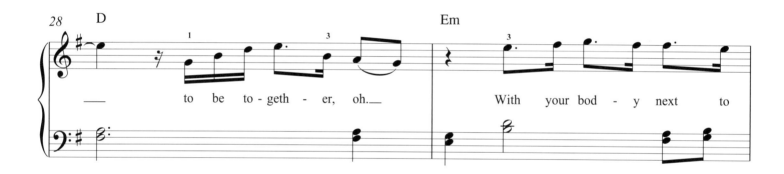

___ to be to - geth - er, oh._ With your bod - y next to

mine, our hearts will beat as one. And we're set_ a - light._ We're a - fire_ love._

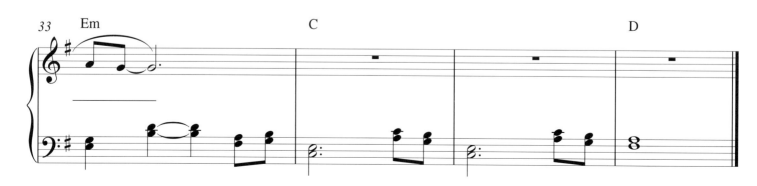

Don't

Words & Music by Ed Sheeran, Ali Jones-Muhammad, Raphael Saadiq, Benjamin Levin, Conesha Owens & Dawn Robinson

With its catchy, chorus-breaking vocal hook, 'Don't' is a song that sticks in your head long after it's passed through your ears, which is fitting given the track's subject matter. The lyrics recount the gory, hurtful details of how Sheeran was cheated on by a former girlfriend and fellow music artist with one of his closest friends.

Hints & Tips: The melody is made up of mostly semiquavers, and it may seem like a lot to fit into each bar! Try listening to the original recording to get a feel for how it goes.

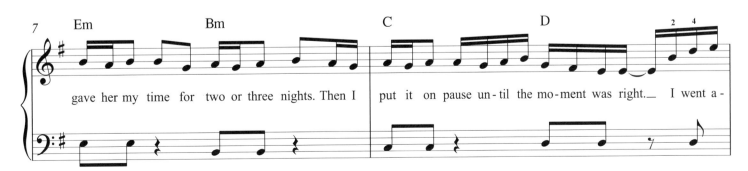

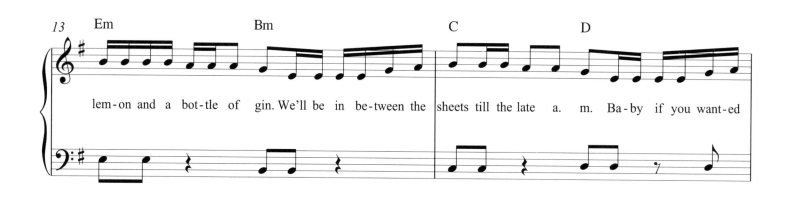

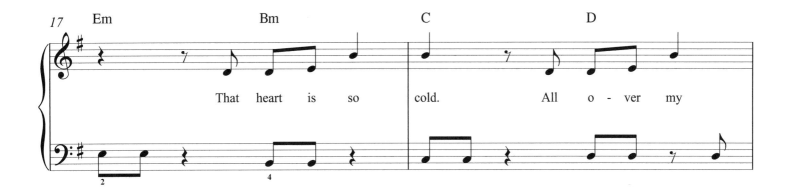

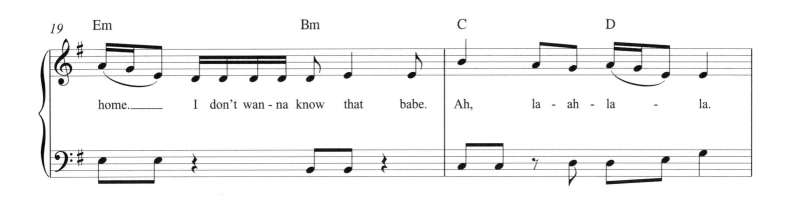

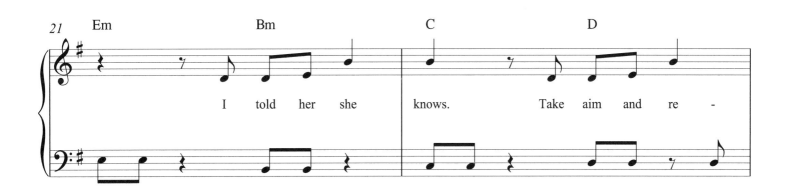

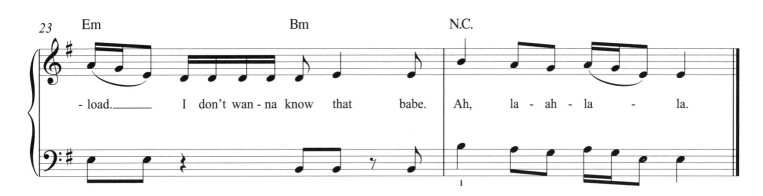

Bloodstream

**Words & Music by Ed Sheeran, Gary Lightbody, Johnny McDaid,
Kesi Dryden, Piers Aggett & Amir Amor**

Never one to shy away from the realities of modern life, in 'Bloodstream' Sheeran explores the escape routes taken by some people to try and flee loneliness through substance abuse. Musically, the song is a tension builder that uses the contrast of the sparse acoustic guitar lines of the verse to make the choruses feel tight and restrained.

Hints & Tips: Once you get the hang of those semiquavers in the left hand, it should make it easier to place the trickier rhythms in the right hand.

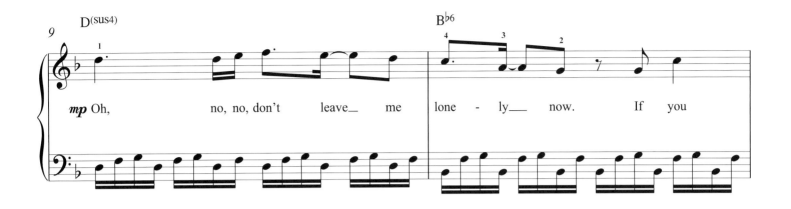

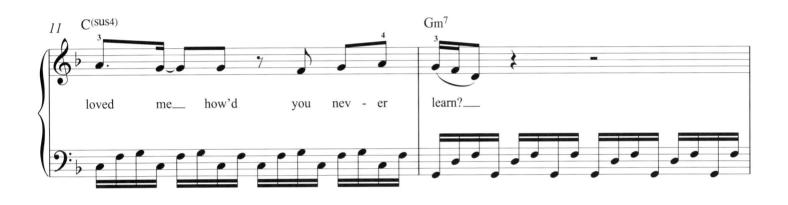

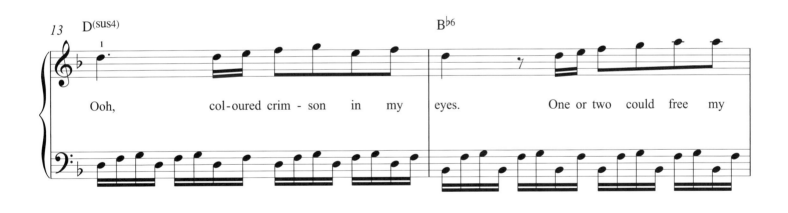

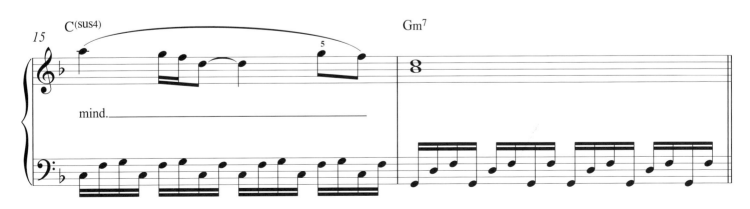

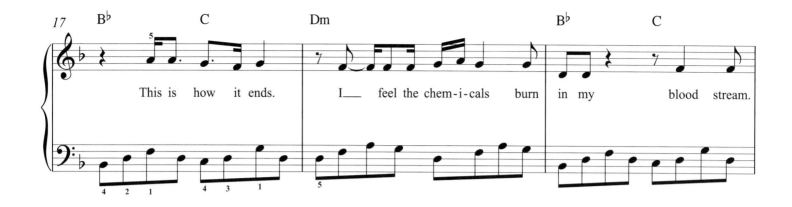

This is how it ends. I___ feel the chem-i-cals burn in my blood stream.

Fad-ing out a-gain, I___ feel the chem-i-cals burn

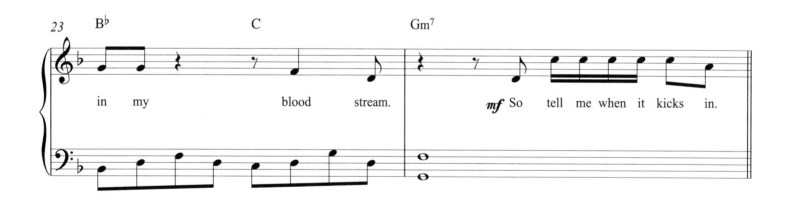

in my blood stream. *mf* So tell me when it kicks in.

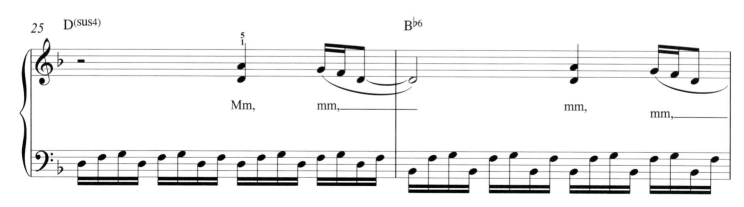

Mm, mm,___ mm, mm,___

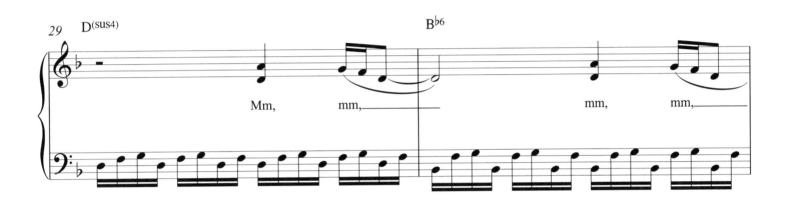

Drunk

Words & Music by Ed Sheeran & Jake Gosling

The fourth single taken from +, 'Drunk' is a song about a self-pitying search for lost love at the bottom of a pint glass. In the accompanying music video, a depressed Sheeran finds he can talk to his cat, and the two proceed to drink a few beers before heading for a night out at a pub and later a house party back at their flat.

Hints & Tips: Check the length of the rest at the beginning of each bar (right hand) as it's different nearly every time! The melody rarely starts on the first beat of the bar.

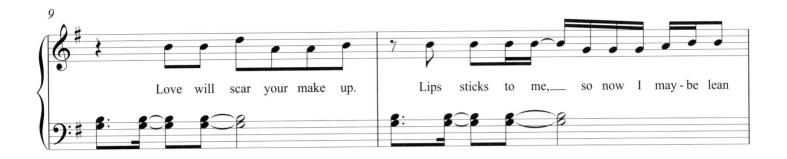

Love will scar your make up. Lips sticks to me,___ so now I may-be lean

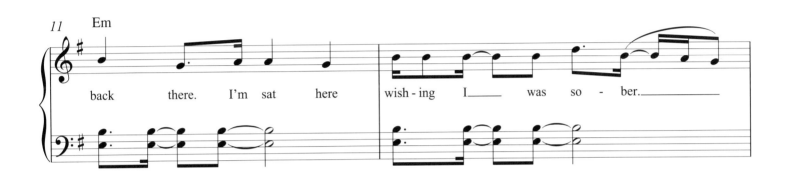

back there. I'm sat here wish-ing I___ was so-ber.___

I know I'll nev-er hold___ you like I used___ to.

But a

mf

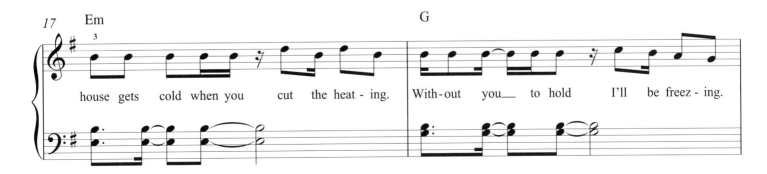

house gets cold when you cut the heat-ing. With-out you___ to hold I'll be freez-ing.

Can't re - ly on my heart to beat__ in 'cause you take parts of it ev - 'ry eve - ning.

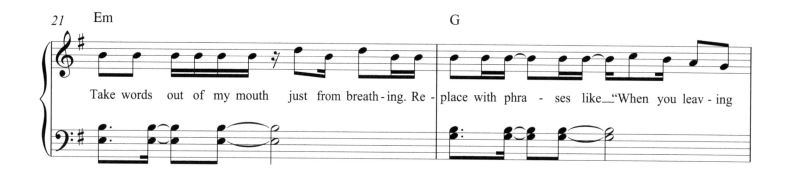

Take words out of my mouth just from breath - ing. Re - place with phra - ses like__ "When you leav - ing

me?" Should I?__ Should I?__ May - be I'll__ get drunk__ a - gain. I'll be

drunk__ a - gain, I'll be drunk__ a - gain to feel a lit - tle

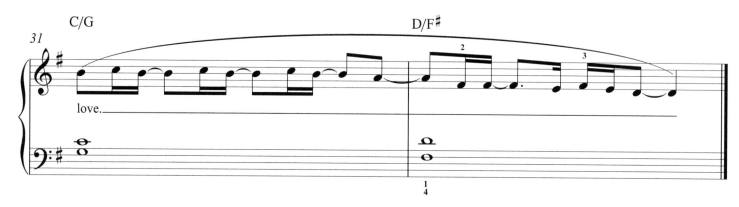

love.__

Grade 8

Words & Music by Ed Sheeran, Robert Conlon
& Sukhdeep Uppal

Sheeran compares the virtuoso abilities of a love interest playing with his heart strings as being akin to the musical skills of someone who has achieved their grade eight certification in this fittingly titled track. Grime producers True Tiger produced the track which was cited in various reviews as one of the highlights of the record.

Hints & Tips: Make sure you don't hold the notes for longer than their full value – the rests are important for creating the feel of the song.

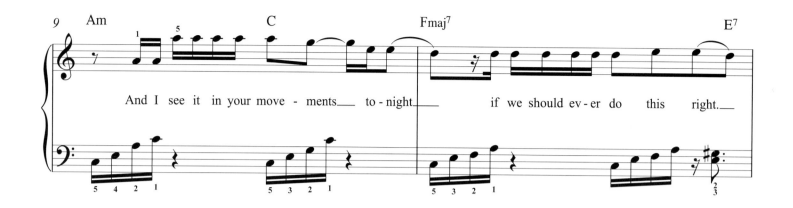

And I see it in your move - ments___ to - night___   if we should ev - er do   this   right.___

I'm nev - er gon - na let   you   down.___   No, I'll nev - er let___ you   down.___

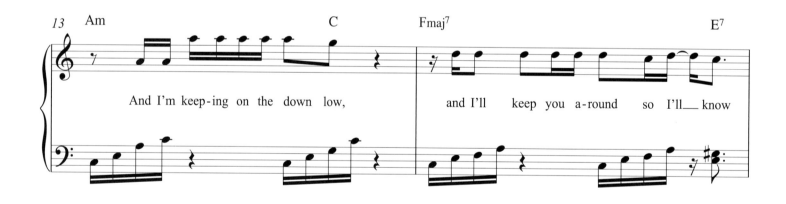

And I'm keep - ing on the down low,   and I'll   keep you a - round   so I'll___ know

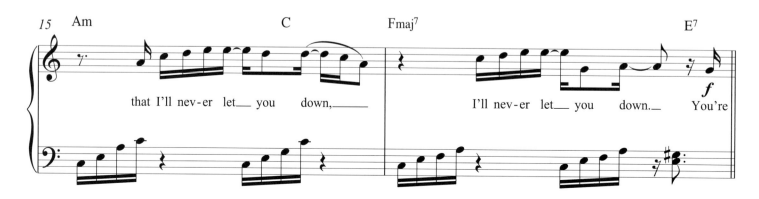

that I'll nev - er let___ you   down,_____   I'll nev - er let___ you   down.___   You're

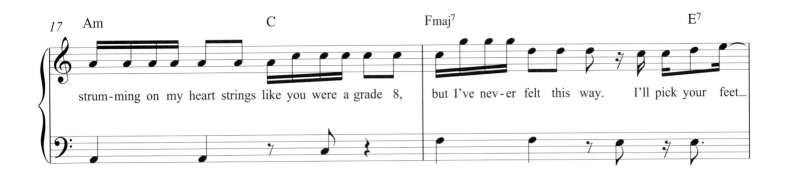

strum-ming on my heart strings like you were a grade 8, but I've nev-er felt this way. I'll pick your feet

___ up off___ of the ground and nev-er, ev-er let you___ down, now. You're

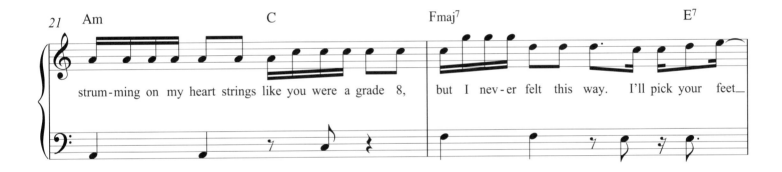

strum-ming on my heart strings like you were a grade 8, but I nev-er felt this way. I'll pick your feet

___ up off___ of the ground and nev-er, ev-er let you down.

Give Me Love

Words & Music by Ed Sheeran, Christopher Leonard
& Jake Gosling

'Give Me Love' is an acoustic guitar-driven balled about a rejected lover who seeks an opportunity to rekindle their stalled relationship and reconfirm that the feelings are still reciprocated. The lyrics also help to set the scene with opening lines that talk about tear-stained t-shirts and a reliance on alcohol to pluck up the courage to reacquaint with this estranged subject of the narrator's affections.

Hints & Tips: Keep the left hand nice and light. It should create a soft, lilting accompaniment for the melody.

I See Fire

Words & Music by Ed Sheeran

An original song written for the soundtrack of Peter Jackson's 2013 Tolkien fantasy epic *The Hobbit: The Desolation of Smaug*, 'I See Fire' scored Sheeran his first No. 1 in New Zealand and was featured in the closing credits of the Hollywood blockbuster. Impressively, it was written and largely recorded in just one day after watching an early cut of the finished film.

Hints & Tips: Figure out what the notes on ledger lines are before you start playing. Write them in pencil if you are unsure, so you can find them quickly and don't interrupt the flow of the melody.

Freely, rubato

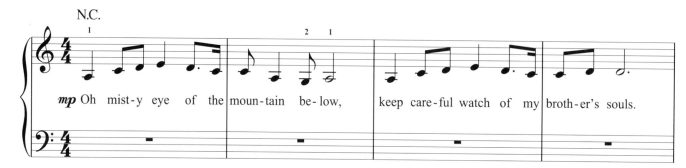

I'm A Mess

Words & Music by Ed Sheeran

Having recording the majority of the tracks on *x* with legendary producer Rick Rubin, it was felt that the record needed something slightly different to round it out and complete the album. Sheeran instead turned to Jake Gosling, who he had worked with on +, to produce this new song.

Hints & Tips: Make the most of the dynamic contrasts in this song. The chorus should be heavier, but still allow for melody to come through.

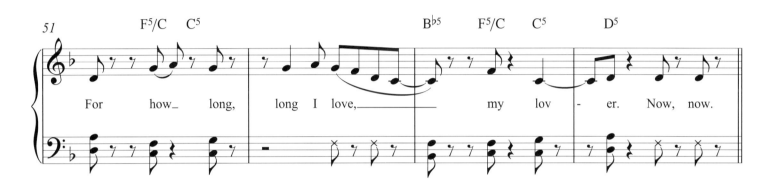

Kiss Me

**Words & Music by Ed Sheeran, Julie Frost
& Justin Franks**

Co-produced by Sheeran and No ID, 'Kiss Me' is a romantic balled about falling head over heels in love set to acoustic guitar, a throbbing, sampled drum track, strings and the occasional outburst of some slick, bluesy electric guitar. The song's lyrics conjure up images of snatched moments of lazy, loved up intimacy between two people only just discovering the extent of their feelings toward one and other.

Hints & Tips: From bar 9, hold the bottom semibreve in the left hand for full the count of the bar while the top part keeps moving.

Lego House

**Words & Music by Christopher Leonard, Ed Sheeran
& Jake Gosling**

A top 5 hit in the UK, Ireland and New Zealand, 'Lego House' was released as the third single from +. The music video to the song features fellow redhead Rupert Grint of Harry Potter fame seemingly pretending to be the singer-songwriter due to their similar appearance before it becomes clear that he's actually an obsessed fan who shares some physical similarities with his idol.

Hints & Tips: Look ahead to the next hand position, so you can be ready whenever you need to cross over your fingers.

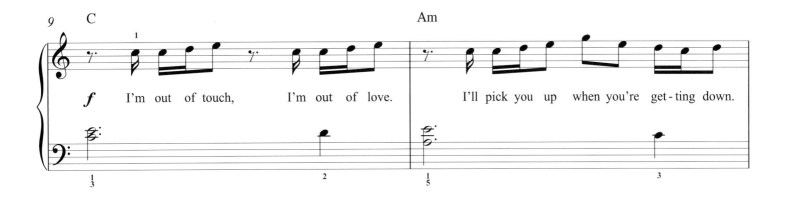

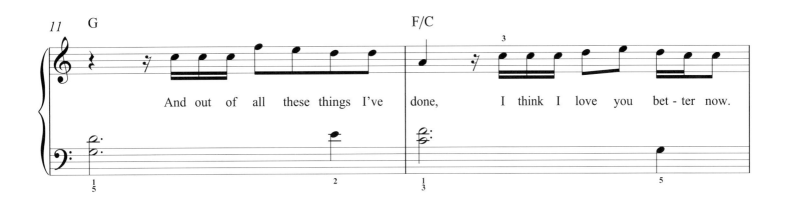

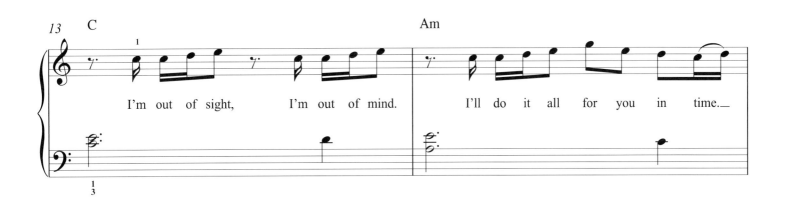

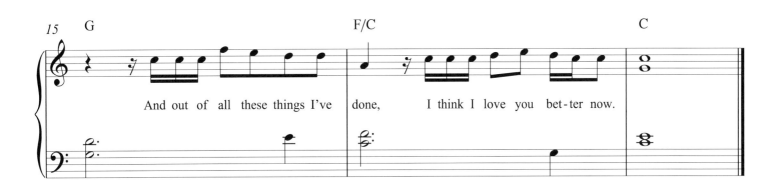

One

Words & Music by Ed Sheeran

'One', the opening track to Sheeran's second album, was surprisingly written prior to the full release of his first record. It is the final song to be penned about the primary love interest that many of the songs on his debut release, +, revolve around and acts as a thread of continuity to link the two albums.

Hints & Tips: There are a lot of tied notes to look out for. Play along with a metronome to help you place the rhythms correctly.

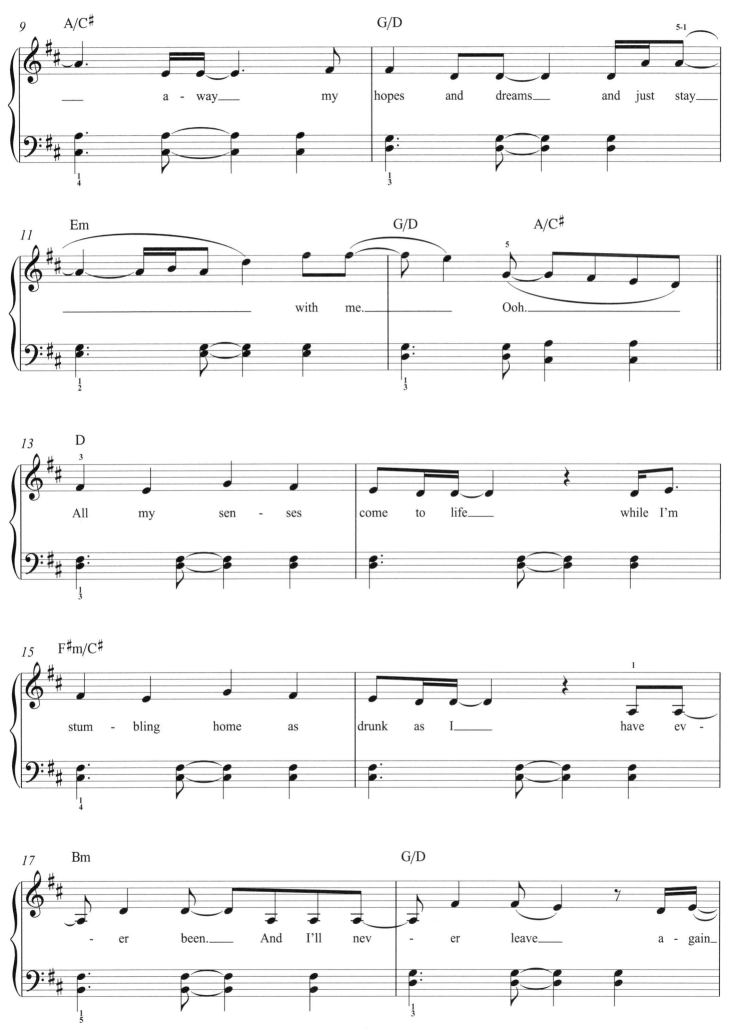

Photograph

Words & Music by Ed Sheeran & Johnny McDaid

Co-written by Johnny McDaid of Snow Patrol, 'Photograph' is the seventh single from Sheeran's second studio album *x*. The lyrics revolve around the idea of a distant or departed love who is all but a memory until they can return. While the track may be a straightforward pop-folk song it also features production by hip hop producers Jeff Bhasker, Emile Haynie and Tyler Sam Johnson.

Hints & Tips: When it comes to the tricky chords in left hand, make sure you know what the notes are and that they all sound precisely together.

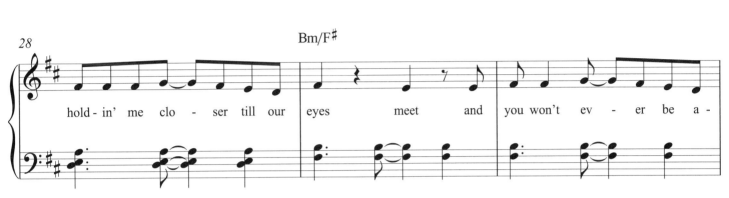

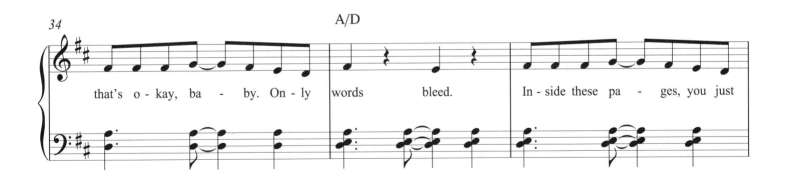

Sing

Words & Music by Pharrell Williams & Ed Sheeran

A No. 1 smash hit in the UK, Ireland, Australia, Canada and Israel, 'Sing' was written by Sheeran and Pharrell Williams who also produced the track. As the lead single from *x*, it represented a major departure in the singer-songwriter's sound, moving away from the folk-pop numbers and shifting him more towards R&B. Critics lauded the fresh change in direction, even going as far as to make comparisons between Sheeran and Justin Timberlake.

Hints & Tips: From bar 5 there are very different things going on in each hand rhythmically, so practice both thoroughly before putting them together. A metronome will help.

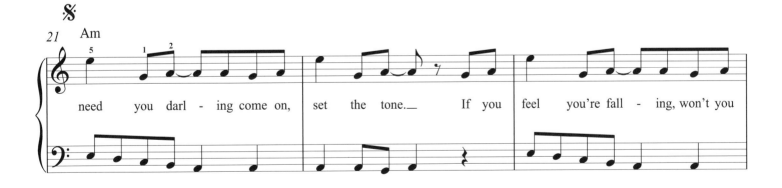

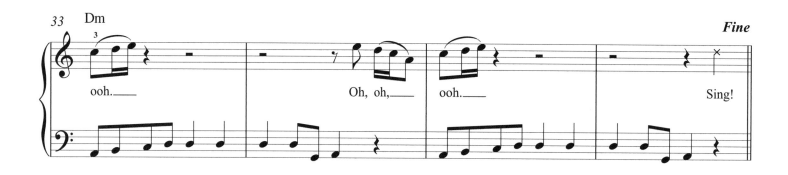

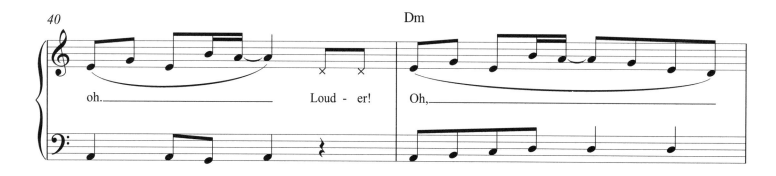

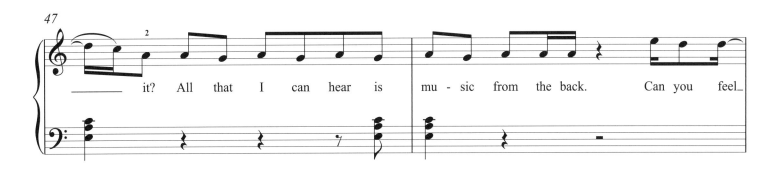

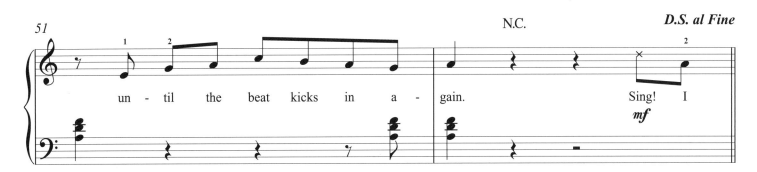

Small Bump

Words & Music by Ed Sheeran

The fifth single taken from +, 'Small Bump' is a heartfelt and sombre song sung from the first-person perspective about a friend who suffered a miscarriage. Interestingly, though written about such a distressing event, the track is in a major key with lyrics that focus on the desire to protect, support and celebrate the child's short life.

Hints & Tips: This song should be played softly and gently. The steady crotchets in the left hand will help you to place the more syncopated right hand rhythms.

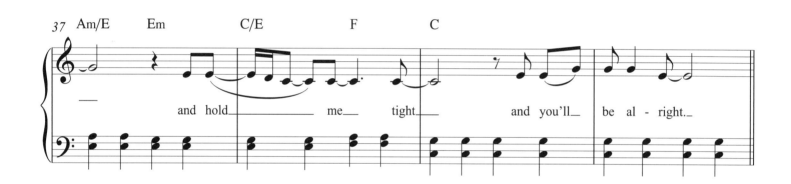

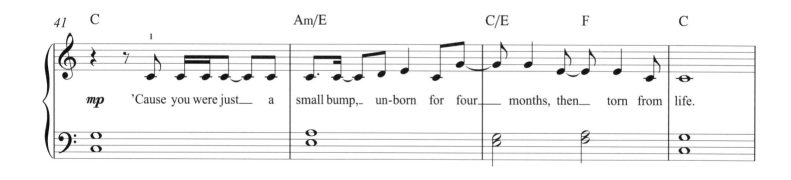

Thinking Out Loud

Words & Music by Ed Sheeran & Amy Wadge

Sheeran famously wrote 'Thinking Out Loud' using a guitar gifted to him by Harry Styles of One Direction, yet piano features heavily on this steady-paced ballad. Like 'I'm a Mess', it was recorded and produced separately from the tracks produced by Rick Rubin, and was one of the last songs to be written on *x*.

Hints & Tips: Make the most of the melody, using dynamics to build up to the chorus in bar 25, which should be loud but expressive.

Tenerife Sea

Words & Music by Ed Sheeran, Johnny McDaid & Foy Vance

Though not released as an independent single, album track 'Tenerife Sea' entered the UK singles chart due to strong download sales following the release of Sheeran's second album, *x*, in June 2014. It was co-written by Johnny McDaid of Snow Patrol and Foy Vance, with production from Rick Rubin.

Hints & Tips: From bar 25, stress the first bottom note of the left hand every time it changes, to create an ascending bass line pattern (F, G, Bb).

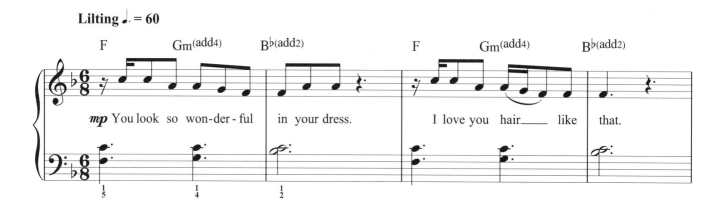

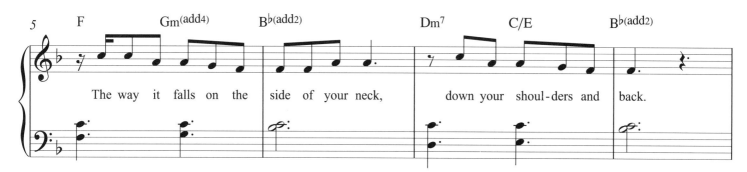

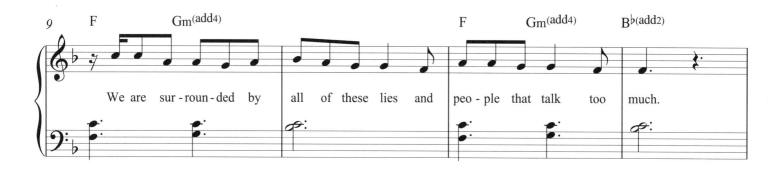

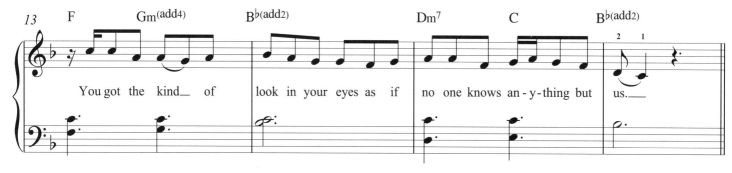

U.N.I

Words & Music by Ed Sheeran & Jake Gosling

'U.N.I' is a song about breaking up with a girlfriend who had departed for university, creating an impassable barrier for their relationship to continue amid the discomfort of being involved in the alien campus culture as an outsider. While it was never released as a single, the fast raps that Sheeran switches into during the verses became a hallmark of his early style and helped establish him as one of the most interesting artists around.

Hints & Tips: The left hand has some important melodic phrases, for example bars 2 and 4. Bring these parts out slightly, but be careful not to drown out the tune in the right hand.

6 7 8 9

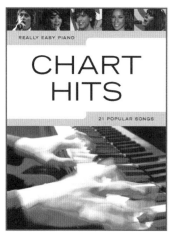

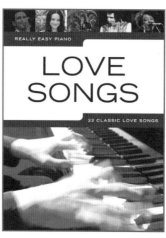
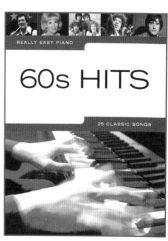
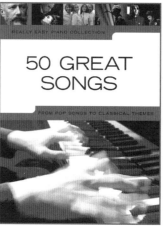
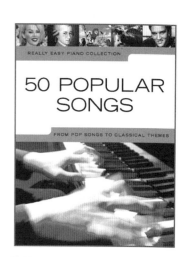